AESOP'S FABLES

Who's book?

marty's book

Rainey

AESOP'S FABLES

TOLD BY VALERIUS BABRIUS

TRANSLATED BY DENISON B. HULL

DECORATIONS BY RAINEY BENNETT

THE UNIVERSITY OF CHICAGO PRESS

LIBRARY OF CONGRESS CATALOG NUMBER: 60-14237

THE UNIVERSITY OF CHICAGO PRESS, CHICAGO 37
CAMBRIDGE UNIVERSITY PRESS, LONDON, N.W. 1, ENGLAND
THE UNIVERSITY OF TORONTO PRESS, TORONTO 5, CANADA

© 1960 BY THE UNIVERSITY OF CHICAGO
PUBLISHED 1960. COMPOSED AND PRINTED BY
THE UNIVERSITY OF CHICAGO PRESS,
CHICAGO, ILLINOIS, U.S.A.

# PREFACE

A figure draped in a raw shade of mustard yellow with a face that was neither human nor yet quite simian, but partook of the worst qualities of both man and ape, leered at me from the red cover of the book of fables which I owned as a child. Not only was the figure hideous, but the colors were so intense that whenever I jiggled the book, this evil spirit came to life and shifted back and forth, so that in order not to have to look at it, I had to hold the book face down and open it from the back.

Who or what was this figure? I supposed that it was the author, for the title of the book was *Æsop's Fables*, and as there was no relation between the figure on the cover and any of the fables inside, I assumed, of course, that it was a picture of the Æsop which had written them. I had no idea what an Æsop was; it evidently wasn't a man; and yet it wasn't an ape either. The cabalistic symbol Æ frightened me, even though the author wrote a "moral" after each fable. But as the book had no preface and no introduction, and as I was convinced that the Thing on the cover was the author, I asked no questions, and so I didn't learn the truth about Aesop for years.

Children today are not subjected to the same terrors, not because books are better designed and covers better drawn, but because Aesop's fables have all but disappeared from the bookstores. You can, of course, find various editions in the public libraries, including perhaps the one which frightened me, but if you ask for Aesop in a bookstore, you will probably find no more than one good prose paraphrase, if that, and nothing that pretends to be a translation from original sources. Now stories that are told and retold many times have a way of changing; sometimes they are better, and sometimes worse; sometimes the emphasis is shifted until the whole point is changed; sometimes the story is shrunk until it is no more than a proverb; sometimes a proverb is blown up into an elaborate story; and, of course, a copy of a copy is almost certain to lose crispness of outline. To recapture the original flavor of Aesop's fables, we must return to original sources. It would be nice to know what Aesop himself wrote.

Alas! So far as we know, Aesop never wrote anything at all! We believe, from what Herodotus tells, that he was a Greek who lived from about 620 to about 560 B.C., and that he told fables. We know that beginning about 400 B.C. almost all fables were ascribed to Aesop, and that these fables were written down, being sometimes quoted singly, as Aristophanes quoted them in his comedies, and being sometimes collected. But in spite of some highly imaginary biographies of Aesop, that is really all that we do know about him. So if we wish to recapture the freshness of his fables as they were first told, we must go to the best of the early writers who collected them in books.

It is only a little over a hundred years ago that our best source was found. In 1840 Abel Villemain, head of the Department of Public Education of the French government, wished to obtain some ancient Greek manuscripts if any could be found, for at that time the Greeks had only recently won their fight for independence from Turkey, and interest in Greek archeology and antiquities was high. So he commissioned a Macedonian Greek, Minoïdes Minas, who had been living in Paris endeavoring to obtain support for the new Greek nation, to go back to his native land to see what he could find. In the Great Lavra, one of the monastic communities on Mount Athos, he found a parchment manuscript, buried in rubbish, containing one hundred and twenty-three fables in Greek verse. Comparison with other manuscripts previously discovered showed at once—for there were duplications of a number of them—that they were the main body of the fables written by Valerius Babrius, an Italian who was a contemporary of Alexander Severus, Roman emperor from A.D. 222 to 235, and were in fact entitled *The Aesopic Fables-in-Verse of Valebrius*, a name evidently the result of telescoping two names—Vale-[rius Ba]brius.

The high literary quality of Babrius' fables was noticed at once. They were poetical and full of beauty and pathos, and far superior to the oldest known version of Aesop, the Latin verses of Phaedrus written about the time of the emperor Tiberius. Where Phaedrus was dull and matter of fact, Babrius was colorful and imaginative, and altogether more representative of the Greek spirit of fable.

Of course Babrius and Phaedrus were not the only ones who collected Aesop's fables, but they were by far the best. Demetrius of Phalerum wrote them down about 300 B.C., although his version has been lost; Avianus wrote them in Latin verse even after Babrius (the date is not certain), although he seems to have merely versified a Latin prose translation of Babrius. Finally, Maximus Planudes, a Byzantine scholar who lived from A.D. 1260 to 1330, made an attempt to collect all the Aesopic fables and to write a life of Aesop; but his life of Aesop is improbable, to say the least, so that doubt is thrown on the accuracy of his fables. But Planudes' version was for many centuries considered the true one, and translations from it were made in many of the tongues of Europe; an English edition was printed by Caxton in 1485. But these are far from being all. Aesop's fables have been used by countless generations of schoolboys as exercises, and countless generations of schoolmasters have required their small charges to put a prose fable into verse, to write a moral to a fable, to write a fable to illustrate a moral, and so forth. The proof of the system is the endless variety of the fragments of fables which have been found.

In the Aesopic tradition each fable is followed by a moral. In the manuscript found by Minas there were morals too, but although written by the same scribe as the body of the fables, there was considerable evidence that they were not written by Babrius himself but had been inserted into the text to conform with tradition. For Babrius wrote his fables as literature, not as lessons, and he does us the honor of assuming that we are intelligent enough to get the point without the necessity of having it rapped on our knuckles. This then is just one more reason for going to Babrius to recapture the freshness of Aesop's stories. Fortunately by doing so we also add more fables to our store.

Phaedrus and Babrius both wrote their fables in verse. So did the greatest of modern fabulists, La Fontaine. Fables, I think, belong in verse because it gives them the epigrammatic quality and crispness they need to point a moral, especially if the moral is not spelled out. In choosing an English verse form suitable for rendering the Greek, I could think of no better model than John Gay's *Fifty-one Fables in Verse*.

The Greek text which I have used is that of W. Gunion Rutherford, M.A., of Balliol College, Oxford, published in 1883. Since the Mount Athos manuscript ends abruptly after only one line of Fable 123, Rutherford used other sources, principally a manuscript found in the Vatican library, in order to complete the collection of fables popularly ascribed to Babrius. The last five are unfortunately only fragments, and although the substance of some of these is known from prose paraphrases, it has so far proved impossible to reconstruct them into verse.

As a reminder to those who are rusty in their mythology, I have appended a glossary of proper names and a brief commentary on a few of the fables. An index to the fables appears at the end of the book.

D. B. H.

Prologue

First was a time when men were sage,
Son Branchus, called the Golden Age,
And in this age of golden hue
The other living creatures knew
Words and articulated sound,
Their forums by the forests bound.
Rocks and pine needles talked, and fish
Could speak, O Branchus, should they wish,
To ship and sailor; sparrows, too,
Could talk as cleverly as you.
The earth but little labor needed
To make things grow as soon as seeded;
And the companionship began
Between the gods and mortal man.
So may you learn these things are true,
And know the stories told to you
By wise old Aesop through the Muse
Of common prose. But I shall use
This honey-dripping comb of speech
Instead, which puts on record each
Of them for you, and thus refines
The harsh iambics' rugged lines.

1. The Bowman and the Lion

A man who shot his bow with skill
Went hunting once upon a hill.
The animals all took to flight,
Spurred in their running by their fright.
A lion stopped, and taking heart,
Challenged the man to fight apart.
"Just wait," the man replied, "and see;
But have no hope for victory.
First meet my envoy so that you
May know exactly what to do."
Then standing to one side a bit,
He shot his bow. The arrow hit,
And pierced the lion's tender side.
The lion in a panic tried
To run away into the wood.
Not far away from him there stood
A fox who urged him to remain,
And to take courage. "Not again,"
The lion answered. "No indeed.
You'll not ensnare me, nor mislead.
His envoy is so sharp, I see
How fearsome he himself must be."

2. The Farmer Who Lost His Hoe

A certain farmer lost his hoe
While digging 'round a vine, and so
He asked the rustics standing by
If they had filched it on the sly.
Each one denied it. Puzzled then
Down to the town he led the men
To take their oaths, for people say
The simple-minded gods are they
Who live on farms; inside the wall
Are truthful gods who notice all.
But as they entered at the gate,
Laid down their knapsacks' heavy weight,
And washed their feet beside the spring,
They heard a herald promising
A thousand drachmas as reward
For plunder stolen from his lord
The god. "So I have come in vain,"
He muttered. "Can the god explain
Another's robbers, even though
He doesn't know his own, and so
Must offer a reward to see
If humans know who they might be?"

3. The Goatherd and His Goat

A goatherd one time shut his herd
Within the fold; but one preferred
To disobey, and munch the green
And luscious herbs in a ravine.
He threw a stone from far away,
And broke her horn—to his dismay.
"Do not, O nanny, fellow thrall,"
He said; "by Pan who watches all,
Do not, I beg you," he implored,
"Betray me, nanny, to your lord.
For when I threw that stone at you
I had not meant to throw so true."
To this the injured goat replied,
"How is it possible to hide
An obvious thing—if I should try it?
The horn will tell, though I keep quiet."

4. The Fisherman

A fisherman took up the net
Which he had only newly set.
It held a great variety
Of dainties living in the sea.
The little fishes fled below
Through mesh so big it let them go;
The big, unable to get by,
Were stretched out in the boat to die.

5. The Cockerels

Tanagra cockerels once fought
With courage many people thought
Equal to men. The vanquished, hurt,
Crouched in the corner in the dirt.
The victor to the housetop sprang,
And flapped his wings, and crowed, and sang,
Until an eagle passing by
Lifted him off into the sky.
The loser, safe upon the ground,
Among the hens walked boldly 'round
In silly pride and self-conceit,
His wages better in defeat.

6. *The Fisherman and the Little Fish*

A fisherman beside the sea
Who scrapes the whole shore thoroughly,
And keeps his sweet life free from need
By only just a slender reed,
Once with a horsehair caught a fish,
A little one, not one you'd wish
To put into the pan and fry;
And thus it begged him with a sigh:
"What profit is there in this thing?
And what the price that I will bring?
I am not fully grown and stout.
My mother seaweed cast me out
Now by this rock. So I implore,
Do throw me back again once more,
For otherwise I'm killed for naught.
But later I am better caught,
When filled with seaweed; I'll be fatter,
And fitter far to fill your platter.
Then come, and take me up again."
So murmuring, it begged in vain,
Gasping for breath. It was not fated
To have its destiny abated;
And as he pierced it with a reed
The old man said, "Who does not heed
The little things unless they're sure
Is fool to hunt when luck's obscure."

7. The Horse and the Ass

A man once had a horse he led
Unburdened by a load. Instead
Upon an ass he put its load.
And growing weary on the road
The ass would come up to the horse
At intervals, and thus discourse:
"If you would like to carry some
Of my big load, I'll not succumb;
I'll quickly be all right. If not,
I'll die upon this very spot."
The other answered, "Go away!
Don't bother me again, I pray."
He crept along in silence, tired,
And finally falling down, expired
As he'd foretold. And so the master,
In order to retrieve disaster,
Brought up the horse, and loosed the pack,
Put the beast's saddle on his back,
And, too, its hide which he had flayed.
"What judgment," said the horse, "I've made!
Now the whole burden I must bear
A part of which I would not share."

8. The Arab and His Camel

An Arab who had put his load
Upon the camel that he rode,
Inquired which way he ought to go,
And whether up or down below.
Not without eloquence it said,
"Well, is the road closed straight ahead?"

9. *The Fisherman Who Played the Flute*

A fisherman beside the sea
Had flutes he played most skilfully,
And hoping many fish would hear
His flutes' sweet music, and draw near
Without his bothering, he laid
His net in place, and gaily played.
Alas! He blew and worked in vain,
But finally had to cast his seine.
This brought him many fish to hand,
And as he saw them on the land
Gasping and flopping every way,
He cleaned his catch, and turned to say,
"Far better had it been for you
To dance when I was playing too,
But since you were not so astute,
You'll have to dance without a flute."

10. *The Slave Girl and Aphrodite*

He loved a filthy, ugly slave,
And everything she asked he gave.
With gold the girl was loaded down,
And trailed a clinging purple gown,
While with the mistress of the place
She joined in battle, face to face.
Then lamps in Aphrodite's honor
She burned for bringing wealth upon her,
And every day she begged, besought,
And sacrificed, and prayed, and fought,
Until the goddess, as they lay
Asleep, came in a dream to say,
"For being fair no thanks you owe.
I'm wroth with him who thinks you so."

11. *The Fox and the Farmer*

A certain farmer wished to shame
A hateful fox that often came
Into his garden and his vines
With wily schemes and bold designs.
He set its tail afire by tying
Some cord to it, and sent it flying.
An overseeing spirit sent
The fox upon its way. It went
To its tormentor's fertile land
Bearing behind a flaming brand.
It was the season of the year
When crops were full, and leaves were sere,
When grain was reaching to the sky,
And hopes for harvests all were high.
The farmer followed, loudly weeping—
Demeter did not see him reaping.

12. *The Swallow and the Nightingale*

A swallow had flown far away
From farm land, and had found one day
A high-voiced nightingale alone
Deep in the woods where she had flown,
Lamenting Itys and the crime
Which took his life before his time.
They knew each other by this tale.
The swallow joined the nightingale,
And chatting, said to her, "My dear,
Is it your living self I hear?
Today's the first time I have seen
You since we were in Thrace. Between
Us there has been some cruel fate
That's kept us both far separate
Even as maidens. Come! Let's go
Down to the farm land here below,
And to the house of man. We'll dwell
As friends and housemates. You shall tell
Your tale to farmers, not to beasts.
Instead of famine you'll have feasts.
Why must your back be frosted white
Each evening, or the bright sunlight
Beat hot upon you? Must you be
Worn out by each adversity?"
The high-voiced nightingale replied,
"Among the rocks let me abide,
Alone and seeming desolate,
And do not try to separate
Me from the mountains. If I can,
I flee from Athens and from man.
The house of man—and men—to me
Mean grief and ancient Tragedy."

13. The Farmer and the Stork

A farmer had light nets prepared
Out in the furrows where they snared
Some cranes, the foes of seeded ground;
And with the cranes a stork was found,
A lame one, injured in the leg.
It humbly turned to him to beg,
"As you can see, I'm not a crane.
My body makes that very plain.
I am a stork, most sacred bird.
I'm no destroyer; that's absurd.
I nurse my father, and take care
Of him when he is ill, I swear."
The other answered, "In what way
You live your life, I cannot say,
O stork. But this I understand:
You're caught with those who rob my land.
This punishment, therefore, you've bought:
You'll be destroyed with those I caught."

14. The Bear and the Fox

He loved a man, a bear once swore,
In marvelous fashion, and what's more,
Would never touch his body, dead.
To this a fox in comment said,
"To snatch a corpse were better than
For you to touch a living man."

15. The Athenian and the Theban

A man from Athens once began
A journey with a Theban man,
And, as you might suppose, was talking.
Their talk was long while they were walking,
And flowing on, it finally came
To heroes. It was all the same,
Long, and in other ways the sort
It is not needful to report.
At last the Theban said he'd call
Alcmene's son greatest of all,
Once of all men, but by all odds
He now was greatest of the gods.
The Athenian could not agree;
Theseus was greater far than he;
The gods had granted him a lot
That was divine; Heracles got
That of a slave. He talked so fast
He won the argument at last.
The other's eloquence was weak;
Being Boeotian he could speak
Only the way a rustic might.
And so he said, to end the fight,
"Have done! You win! Accordingly
Let all the wrath of Theseus be
Turned against us, while Heracles
May turn on Athens if he please."

16. The Nurse and the Wolf

A rustic nurse, her patience failing,
Threatened an infant who was wailing,
"Now stop your crying, or," she lied,
"I'll throw you to the wolf outside!"
The wolf, it happened, heard her threat,
And waited patiently to get
An easy dinner as she'd said,
Until the child was put to bed,
And then he left, and went away.
He'd sat with stupid hopes all day,
And now was famished and in need,
A hungry, gaping wolf indeed.
His mate, the she-wolf, said to him,
"How is it that your catch is slim?"
"And how indeed," the wolf replied,
"When trust in woman was my guide!"

17. The Cat and the Cock

A cat, in order to waylay
Domestic hens throughout the day,
Hung like a bag upon a hook.
A prudent cock, his beak a crook,
Observed, and sneered, and sharply cried,
"In all this world both long and wide
I've never seen a bag like that
Which has the teeth of one live cat."

18. The North Wind and the Sun

Between the North Wind and the Sun
A quarrel rose as to which one
Could strip the mantle from a man
Walking the road. The wind began,
And blew, for in his Thracian way
He thought that he would quickly lay
The wearer bare by force. But still
The man, shivering with the chill,
Held fast his cloak, nor let it go
The more the North Wind tried to blow,
But drew the edges close around,
Sat himself down upon the ground,
And leaned his back against a stone.
And then the Sun peeped out, and shone,
Pleasant at first, and set him free
From the cold blowing bitterly,
And next applied a little heat.
Then suddenly, from head to feet,
By burning fire the man was gripped,
Cast off his cloak himself, and stripped.

19. *The Fox and the Bunch of Grapes*

Upon a mountain side's incline
In clusters on a blackened vine
Hung grapes. The fox, that wily beast,
Observed their fullness now increased,
And thought to leap from tip of toe,
And grasp the fresh fruit from below,
For they were ripe for harvesting.
But he grew tired in vain, his spring
Not strong enough to reach so high.
He salved his grief while going by:
"Just as I thought before I'd seen;
  Those grapes aren't ripe at all, but green!"

20. *The Drover and Heracles*

As he was driving out of town
A drover's wagon tumbled down
Into a yawning hole, but he
Who should have helped, stopped lazily,
And prayed to Heracles for aid—
The only god to whom he prayed.
The god stood near the man, and said,
"Take hold, and turn the wheels ahead,
  And goad the team with might and main.
  Help when you pray, or prayer is vain."

21. The Oxen and the Butchers

The oxen one time sought to slay
The butchers for their hostile way,
And gathering ready for the battle,
They sharpened horns. One of the cattle,
A certain old one who had plowed
Much of the earth, addressed the crowd:
"They cut our throats like experts; so
It does not hurt us when we go.
But if we fall to unskilled men,
Our dying will be double then.
The worshipper will not omit
The ox because the butcher quit."

22. The Man and His Girls

Once on a time there was a man
Whose life was in the middle span;
He was not young, nor old yet quite.
He mixed his black hair up with white,
And had the leisure night and day
For revelry and love and play.
He loved two women, young and old.
The young girl saw him young and bold;
The older woman saw him sage,
A fellow for her in old age.
And so the maiden in her prime
Pulled out his white hairs every time
She found one blossoming—alack!—
The old one only pulled the black,
Until between the two the pair
Had made him bald by pulling hair.

23. *The Drover and the Lion*

A drover lost a long-horned ox,
And sought to find it near some rocks
Far in a distant wood. He swore
That he would lay a ram before
The mountain nymphs as soon as he
Could catch the thief. Unluckily
Just as he went across a mound
He saw his fine ox on the ground
Waiting to be a lion's feast.
Unhappy man, he cursed the beast,
And promised if he got away,
He'd give the nymphs an ox that day.

24. *The Frogs and the Sun*

There was a wedding of the Sun
When summer's season had begun.
The animals were all at play,
And frogs held dances every day
In all the pools. A toad said, "Stop!
This is no time to sing and hop,
But rather time for thought and grief.
If he alone dries every leaf,
And withers every pool, think well
What evils we should have to tell
If when he's married he begot
A child just like him—and as hot."

25. The Hares and the Frogs

The hares resolved to live no more,
But cast themselves at once from shore
Into the water of the pools,
For they are craven creatures, fools,
And cowardly of spirit; they
Know only how to run away.
But when they reached the broad pond's side
Where throngs of little frogs abide,
And saw them jumping from the bank
Into the deep mud, rank on rank,
They stopped, and one hare, taking heart,
Said, "Comrades, let us now depart.
No longer need we die. I see
Others are feebler far than we."

26. The Cranes and the Farmer

Cranes occupied a farmer's place
Seeded with wheat. So to give chase
The farmer shook an empty sling
That seemed to them a fearsome thing.
But as they faced him while he threw
The breezes at them, they soon knew
That they would never need to flee
Again in future; until he,
As he had never done before,
Threw stones, and beat them hard and sore.
They left his field behind with screams:
"Flee to the Pygmies' lands! It seems
This man's not satisfied to scare—
He's starting now to act. Beware!"

27. The Weasel That Was Caught

By trick someone had caught and bound
A wretched weasel which he drowned
In water underneath the banks
Where the glens meet. It said, "Poor thanks
You pay for help like hunting mice
And lizards." "But you have one vice,"
He answered. "I bear witness you
Have helped. Unfortunately, too,
You strangled all the hens we own,
Laid bare the whole house to the bone,
And harmed considerably more
Than you had ever helped before."

28. The Ox and the Toad

An ox while drinking by the road
Stepped on the offspring of a toad.
His mother came; he was not there;
She asked her sons if they knew where
He was. "O Mother, he is dead.
We saw a ponderous quadruped
An hour ago who came this way,
Whose hoof quite squashed him where he lay."
The toad then puffed herself all out,
And asked if it had been about
This size. They told their mother, "Stop,
Lest you be torn apart! You'll pop
To bits before you imitate
A creature so immensely great."

29. The Old Horse

An ancient horse one time was sold
For grinding grain, he was so old;
And he was harnessed to a mill
To work all evening until
He groaned, and said, "Oh, what a race!
I'm running circles in one place,
And turning 'round the goal ahead,
Just running for my daily bread!"

30. Hermes and the Sculptor

A certain sculptor once assayed
To sell a Hermes he had made,
Carved of white marble, and two men
Both wished to buy it there and then,
One for a tombstone (for his son
Had lately died), the other one,
A craftsman, wished to dedicate
The marble as a god. 'Twas late,
And still the sale did not proceed
Because the sculptor had agreed
To give the men another view
Of Hermes in the morning too.
But while he slept, the sculptor saw
Hermes himself in splendor draw
Himself up by the gates of dreams,
And say, "So be it. Weigh your schemes.
One or the other, I'm afraid,
A god or corpse, I shall be made."

31. The Weasels and the Mice

The weasels and the mice waged war
Implacably, with blood and gore;
The weasels always won the fight.
The mice believed their sorry plight,
The cause of their defeat, no doubt,
Was that their generals weren't marked out;
They were unorganized, and waited
'Til dangers had accumulated.
And so they chose for eminence
In family, strength, and common sense
Those noblest on the battlefield.
These armed them all with spear and shield,
And organized their ranks anew
By phalanx, regiment, platoon,
And squad and company. As soon
As everything was organized,
And all assembled as advised,
A certain mouse, who'd taken heart,
Challenged his weasel counterpart.
Each general upon his head
Fixed straw from walls of mud, and led
Them on, outstanding in the throng.
But once again their plans went wrong:
Again rout overtook the mice.
Now others with no such device
Escaped in safety down their holes,
But the strange straw upon their polls
Forbade the generals getting through,
And running down a mousehole too.

32. The Weasel and Aphrodite

A weasel one time loved a man
Of pleasing looks and fitting clan,
And Cypris, mother of desire,
Granted the creature to acquire
A woman's form, like maiden fair,
For whom no man would fail to care.
He saw her, and she won his heart.
Their marriage was about to start,
The banquet brought before the house,
When past them ran a little mouse.
Down from her deep-strewn couch the bride
Leaped in pursuit. Thus set aside,
The banquet was abandoned. Love,
Who'd looked so smiling from above,
And played so prettily, departed,
By Nature beaten and outsmarted.

33. The Farmer, the Boy, and the Jackdaws

The Pleiades had gone below:
It was the time of year to sow
Seed in the fields, and by the wheat
He'd sown in furrows at his feet
A farmer stood on guard. Indeed
There came, and fell upon the seed,
A multitudinous company
Of black and most disorderly
Loud screaming jackdaws, and a crew
Of hungry, evil starlings, who
Were seeking food they could destroy.
And with the farmer went a boy
Who carried in his hand a sling.
Each time he told the boy to bring
This weapon to him, every bird
Fled ere he took it, for they heard.
The farmer thought, and then began
Explaining a much better plan.
"Boy, we must fool this clever breed;
So when they come, I shall proceed
By asking for a loaf of bread,
But you shall give the sling instead."
The birds blew in from every hand;
He asked for bread as they had planned;
The boy then handed him the sling
Filled up with stones so it would sting,
And then he threw it, hitting one
Upon the head, enough to stun,
Another on the leg, a third
Upon the shoulder. Every bird
Bombarded so from foot to head
Flew from the place in haste, and fled.

34. *The Child Who Ate the Insides*

A country mob, when crops were full,
Unto Demeter slew a bull.
Their threshing floor was strewn with vines,
Tables of meats, and jars of wines.
Among the children there was one
Who stuffed as if he'd ne'er be done
On all the tripe he could partake,
Departing with a stomach ache.
Into his mother's arms he fell,
And cried, "O Mother, sad to tell,
I'm dying, for without a doubt
My insides all are coming out."
His mother answered, "Child, take heart.
Throw up, nor spare a single part.
For these are not your own insides,
My child, but those the bull provides."

35. *The Ape's Two Sons*

Two sons the ape brings forth, but she
Who bears them is not equally
Maternal to them; for the one
With fatal kindness overdone,
She smothers in her savage breast;
The other, without interest,
She casts aside as overplus,
As useless and superfluous.
And he to whom she nothing gives
Goes to the wilderness, and lives.

36. *The Tree and the Reeds*

The wind once lifted up a tree
By root and branch for all to see;
Then tore it from the mountain side,
And gave it to the brook, to ride
The billowing waves, swept on before,
A giant thing which men of yore
Had planted. By the river bank
Were many reeds which stood, and drank
The quiet water peacefully.
Astonishment then gripped the tree
That, though the reeds were weak and frail,
They were not broken by the gale,
Although an oak so very stout
Had thus itself been rooted out.
And then the reeds with wisdom said,
"Be not astonished or misled.
The wind has conquered you with ease;
You see when we just feel a breeze,
We bend to it with soft compliance,
While you've been battling in defiance."

37. The Young Bull and the Ox

A young bull still unchafed by yoke
Was ranging in the fields, and spoke
Thus to an ox who dragged a plow:
"Poor wretch, to have to labor now!"
The old ox, silent in his toil,
Just kept on turning up the soil.
But when the country people went
To make a sacrifice, they sent
The old ox out to pasture, loose,
But caught the young bull in a noose,
And with his horns well roped and tied,
They brought him to the altar side
To spill his blood. The other said,
"They fed you up for this, instead
Of working. Though you pass us by,
You're sacrificed while young, and die.
What rubs the sinews of your backs
Is not the yoke. It is the ax."

38. The Woodcutters and the Pine

Woodcutters splitting a wild pine
Drove wedges made from it, in line,
To split it, so their work would be
Done later much more easily.
The wild pine moaned, "How can I blame
The ax? It doesn't even claim
A kinship with my stock, as do
These wedges I am mother to.
For driven home from every side
They certainly will split me wide."

39. The Whales, the Dolphins, and the Crab

The whales and dolphins disagreed.
A crab passed by them, for his breed
Was trash in the community;
And then as mediator, he
Restored these princes to their senses,
And reconciled their differences.

40. The Philosophic Camel

A camel with a hump once crossed
A river where swift currents tossed.
She emptied. But her droppings passed her,
And went before her somewhat faster.
"I'm truly badly off," she said,
"What was behind me's now ahead."

41. The Lizard and the Snakes

Across the back a lizard breaks
When stretching to the length of snakes.
You'll harm yourself—that's all you'll do—
By matching better men than you.

42. The Man and the Dog

He sacrificed to gods, and then
A brilliant banquet gave to men.
His dog turned up a canine friend,
And asked the latter to attend.
The latter came; and booting hard,
The cook propelled him from the yard.

43. *The Deer and the Hounds*

An antlered deer, who was accursed
Under the scorching heat by thirst,
Saw his reflection just beyond
While drinking water in a pond.
By hooves and feet he was distressed,
But plumed himself that he was dressed
In antlers that were truly fair.
But Nemesis was standing there.
For of a sudden the deer found
Men hunting him with net and hound;
And when he saw, he quickly fled,
Not stopping for a drink. Instead
He flew across the plain, and then,
On coming to the woods again,
His antlers caught in shrub and tree.
He said, "Unhappily for me
I've been deceived. The feet I hated
Were saving me. But now I'm fated
To be delivered to the crowd
By that of which I was so proud."

44. *The Three Bulls and the Lion*

Three bulls were grazing every day
Together while a lion lay
In wait to catch them. But, thought he,
He simply could not catch all three.
So using festering calumnies
He turned them into enemies,
And separating each from each,
He had three meals in easy reach.

45. *The Goats and the Goatherd*

Zeus scattered snow. A goatherd fled,
And drove his goats, all overspread
With thick white covering of snow,
Into a lonesome cave below.
And finding there had gone before
A herd of wild horned goats, both more
And bigger than his own, he sought
Young branches from the woods, and brought
And threw them in as feed. His own
He cast adrift to starve alone.
As it cleared off he found his dead;
The others did not wait. Instead
They sought the ungrazed groves that stand
On inaccessible mountain land.

46. *The Sick Deer*

His nimble limbs grown stiff with pain
A deer lay in the verdant plain,
Deep in the mastic from which he
Had ready forage if need be.
And herds of dappled beasts drew nigh
To see their harmless neighbor lie,
And each one nibbled of his grass,
And went off toward the woods. Alas,
They did not notice he was dying.
A wasted skeleton he's lying,
Not from disease, but hunger, dead,
His second fourth of life not sped,
Who, had he never been befriended,
Had lived until old age descended.

47. *The Old Man and His Children*

Among the ancients was a man
Who'd lived a very goodly span,
And who had children numberless.
And when he made his last address
(For death was near him where he stood),
He urged them bring some rods of wood
If there were any anywhere;
And someone found, and brought some there.
"Now try for me with all your might
To break rods bound together tight."
They could not do so. "Now try one,"
And that was very quickly done.
He said, "Now children, as you see,
When all of you alike agree,
No one, it matters not how strong,
Can ever do you any wrong.
But surely if you're separated,
You'll be, like this, annihilated."

48. Hermes and the Dog

A bust of Hermes, square below,
Stood by the road where travelers go,
Stones heaped beneath it in a pile.
A dog came, saying with a smile,
"First, Hermes, greetings. Next, may I
Anoint you, thus not passing by
A god who's god of wrestling too?"
The god replied to him, "If you
Don't lick this olive oil from me,
Or sprinkle on me, I shall be
Most grateful. But I must implore,
Please honor me with nothing more."

49. The Workman and Luck

One night a workman sat too near
A well, and soon he seemed to hear
The voice of Luck beside him say,
"You there! Wake up! And listen, pray!
I warn you now that if you fall,
I shall be blamed by one and all,
For surely they will pick on me.
My reputation's bad. You see
I am accused of everything
Collectively, should people bring
Misfortunes on themselves at all,
No matter how such things befall."

50. The Fox and the Woodcutter

A fox was fleeing. As she fled
A hunter fast behind her sped.
But being wearied, when she spied
An old man cutting wood, she cried,
"By all the gods that keep you well,
Hide me among these trees you fell,
And don't reveal the place, I pray."
He swore that he would not betray
The wily vixen; so she hid,
And then the hunter came to bid
The old man tell him if she'd fled,
Or if she'd hidden there. He said,
"I did not see her," but he showed
The place the cunning beast was stowed
By pointing at it with his finger.
But still the hunter did not linger.
He put no faith in leering eye,
But trusting in the words, went by.
Escaped from danger for a while
The fox peeked out with coaxing smile.
The old man said to her, "You owe
Me thanks for saving you, you know."
"Most certainly; for I was there
As witness of your expert care.
But now farewell. And don't forget,
The god of oaths will catch you yet
For saving with your voice and lips
While slaying with your finger tips."

51. The Widow and the Sheep

A certain widow used to keep
Within her house a woolly sheep,
And, wishing that she might increase
The harvest that she took of fleece,
She clipped it utterly, and sheared
Its wool so close its flesh appeared,
And even cut the creature's hide.
In pain the injured sheep then cried,
"Do not maltreat me. If I bleed
Is that the thing you want or need?
But, mistress, if you want some meat,
There is a butcher down the street
Who'll sacrifice me instantly.
But if you need some wool from me,
Or fleece, not flesh, again I say,
There is a barber down the way
Who'll clip my wool to give to you,
And leave me quite uninjured, too."

52. The Wagon and the Oxen

Some oxen drew a four-wheeled cart
To town. And from the very start
It squeaked aloud. So, seized by wrath,
The wagoner stood in the path,
And said, "O wickedest indeed
Of my possessions, do you need
To groan when carried up the hill
On others' shoulders—who keep still?"

53. The Fox and the Wolf

A hapless fox once chanced to meet
A wolf, and begged that he would treat
Her with some mercy, spare her still,
Respect her age, and please not kill.
He said, "I will, by Pan, if you
Will tell me three things that are true."
"First, then, I wish you'd never met me;
And, second, were too blind to get me;
And third," she said, "another year
You wouldn't live to meet me here."

54. The Eunuch and the Seer

A eunuch asked a seer the chances
Of children in his circumstances.
Spreading a sacred liver, he,
The seer, replied to him, "I see,
When looking at this sacred meat,
A father who is quite complete;
But when it is your face I scan,
You do not seem to be a man."

55. The Ox, the Ass, and the Old Man

He yoked his ox up with his ass;
They made a team that needs must pass,
Though beggarly. When work was through,
And he prepared to loose the two,
The ass would stop the ox, and say,
"Who'll bring the old man's gear today?"
The ox's answer to her was,
"He who inevitably does."

56. Zeus and the Ape

Zeus was awarding to all creatures
Prizes for children with fair features,
And looked at each to judge its shape.
There also came an ugly ape
As if she were a lovely mother,
And in her bosom held another,
A naked little snub-nosed thing.
And then the heavens began to ring
With the gods' laughter at the sight;
But thus she spoke, "Zeus knows who's right,
And who's the winner; but, you see,
This child's most beautiful to me."

57. Hermes' Wagon and the Arabs

Hermes once piled a wagon high
With villainy, deceit, and lie
Of every sort; and drove it through
The world. And, as there came in view
Tribe after tribe, with thought he cast
Some of his wares to each; then passed
Into the Arabs' country, where
They emptied it, nor let it fare
Forth on the road ahead, although
There still were places it might go.
Hence Arabs are, as I have learned
By long experience sadly earned,
Liars and cheats in every wise
Upon whose tongues truth never lies.

58. Hope among Men

Zeus once collected in a jar
All of the useful things there are,
And put it covered up beside
A man, who by temptation tried,
And keen to know just what it hid,
With weakened will removed the lid,
And let the contents out to fly
To the gods' dwellings in the sky.
But Hope alone was left within,
Caught by the cover, and kept in
When he had put it on again.
So Hope remains behind with men,
Pledged to give each the useful things
Which had escaped from us on wings.

59. Zeus, Poseidon, and Athena

Zeus and Poseidon, so they say
(And with them was a third that day,
Athena), once were arguing
Which could create the finest thing.
So Zeus made first (for he began)
A most amazing creature, Man;
Pallas a house where Man might live;
Poseidon chose a bull to give.
Among them Momus judged, for he
Still dwelt with gods, a deity.
But as his nature was, all full
Of hatred, he disliked the bull.
Its horns he wanted on its face
Below its eyes, a perfect place,
Permitting it to see to strike.
The man also he did not like
Because there wasn't any door
Or window in his bosom for
Observing what his neighbor thought;
The house condemned at once as nought
Because there were no wheels below
In case its master wished to go
Off traveling from place to place,
And thus could move it on apace.

60. The Greedy Mouse

A mouse fell in a jar of sauce
That he found open—to his loss.
And as he drowned, and as he died,
These were the final words he cried:
"On every sort of meat I've dined;
On every sort of drink I've wined;
I'm filled with all a mouse might try.
It's fitting now for me to die."

61. The Hunter and the Fisherman

A hunter always came each day
Back home from hunting far away
Up in the mountains; and there came
A fisherman who did the same
When he had satisfied his wish
To fill his basket full of fish.
And somehow these two chanced to meet.
The hunter thought he'd rather eat
Some of the fish from out the sea;
The fisherman in turn said he
Preferred wild game; so both were glad,
And gave each other what they had.
Now soon the two of them arranged
So things should always be exchanged,
And had their dinners pleasantly
'Til someone said to them, "You'll see
How habit spoils the benefit
Of your exchange. You'll tire of it,
And then you both will seek once more
The very things you had before."

62. The Mule

A mule was eating grain and hay
Out of his idle trough one day,
And having finished, ran along,
And kicked his heels, and brayed this song;
"My mother, mind you, is a horse,
And I can run as swift a course."
But then he stopped. He had, alas,
Recalled his father was an ass.

63. The Hero

There was a hero once who stayed
Within the house of one who prayed,
A pious man, who had a shrine
Within his courtyard where with wine
He drenched the altars, scented, spiced,
And wreathed them when he sacrificed.
He prayed, "O dearest hero, see
If you can do good things for me."
The hero in the depth of night
Replied, "We heroes can't requite
With blessings, friend. For these things go
And ask the gods. Indeed, you know,
We give all evils, those that stay
With men. If you want evils, pray.
And with your wish will soon come true.
I've many more than one for you."

64. *The Berry Bush and the Silver Fir*

A berry bush and silver fir
Once quarreled; he had slandered her.
The fir replied by singing praise,
Lauding herself in many ways,
"Oh, I am beautiful and tall;
I grow the straightest of them all,
And with the very clouds I live;
Long rafters to the roofs I give,
And keels to ships; of all the trees
Most suitable and like to please."
The berry bush replied to her,
"If you would just remember, fir,
How often axes fell a tree,
You'd rather be a bush like me."

65. *The Crane and the Peacock*

A crane with color dull and ashen
Once quarreled with that plate of fashion,
The peacock, which shook wings of gold.
"But with these wings at which you scold,"
The ashen-colored creature said,
"Because their color's gray and dead,
I press the stars, and loudly cry,
While you are never seen on high.
You flap your gilded wings around
Just like a rooster on the ground."

66. The Two Packs

Among the gods when time began
Prometheus lived. He made a man
All molded out of earth and plaster,
And thus produced for beasts a master.
He hung on him two packs to wear,
Filled with the woes that men must bear,
With strangers' woes the one before,
But that in back, which carried more,
Was filled with evils all his own.
Hence many men, I think, are prone
To see the ills some other bears
But still be ignorant of theirs.

67. The Lion and the Ass

A lion and an ass became
Partners in hunting other game.
Of strength the lion had the most;
A fleeter foot the ass could boast.
So when their plunder was enough,
The lion meted out the stuff
In separate portions: there were three.
"The first," he said, "belongs to me
Because I'm king. The second, too,
As equal partner here with you.
The third will give you grievous trouble
Unless you leave me at the double."

68. *Apollo and Zeus*

To all the gods Apollo said,
While shooting arrows far ahead,
"No one can shoot as far as I—
Not with a bow. Just let him try!"
Zeus differed, although playfully,
With Phoebus, and would not agree.
Then they drew lots, which Hermes took,
Put into Ares' cap, and shook;
And Phoebus drew the lot. He drew
His bow into a circle, too;
And sped its missile, as a test,
Into the Gardens of the West.
Zeus took his stance, his legs astride,
The measure of it just as wide
As Phoebus' shot, and said, "My son,
Where shall I shoot? Of room there's none."
He won the victory, although
He never even shot his bow.

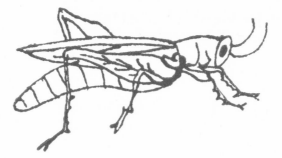

69. The Hound and the Hare

A certain hound, one not untried
In hunting, thrust a bush aside,
And started up a little hare
With shaggy feet in hiding there;
Pursuing her he lost the race.
A goatherd watching said, "Her pace
Turned out to be too fast for you."
He said, "That certainly is true.
You see, one runs a certain way
When catching something, as in play,
But in another fashion still
When fleeing from impending ill."

70. The Wedding of the Gods

The gods are marrying, and Ares,
As each is joined in wedlock, marries
That arrogant, bold wanton, Pride,
On the last lottery for a bride.
He loves her, everybody knows,
And follows everywhere she goes.

71. The Farmer and the Sea

A farmer saw a sea-borne ship
That carried sailors sometimes dip
A curling wave up with its prow,
And said, "O sea, I pray somehow
You never need be sailed again,
Element pitiless to men."
The sea, however, heard, and said,
"Pray do not curse me. You're misled.
For I should not be blamed by you
For any of the things I do.
The winds are all to blame, not I,
The winds among whose blasts I lie;
For if you see me, and you sail
Without the winds, you cannot fail
To say that I am gentler still
Than all the rugged land you till."

72. The Jackdaw and the Birds

That shining herald of the skies,
Bright Iris, once announced a prize
Throughout the gods' ethereal hall.
And straightway she was heard by all,
And all had longing for the gift.
A spring was trickling through a rift
In rock too rugged for a goat,
And water in a quiet moat
Lay clear and summery, 'til a flock
Of many birds came to the rock,
And washed their legs, and bathed their cheeks,
Shook wings, and gave their plumage tweaks.
And to that spring a jackdaw went,
Son of a crow, and old and spent,
Who, plucking here and there a feather,
Inserted all of them together
Into his supple shoulders. He
Alone wore each one's finery.
Then, stronger than an eagle, darted
Up to the gods, and thus departed.
Zeus was astonished at the sight,
And would have given the prize outright
If a quick swallow in the guise
Of Pallas with the bright gray eyes
Had not brought shame upon the bird.
She pulled his feathers: in a word
She stripped his falsehood to the bone,
And made the jackdaw really known.

73. The Kite

A kite, just like another bird,
Had a shrill voice. But when he heard
A horse that whinnied musically,
He mimicked it, but found that he
Got neither what he wanted, nor
Retained the voice he had before.

74. The Horse, the Bull, the Dog, and the Man

A dog, a bullock, and a horse,
Fatigued by cold upon their course,
Once happened on a poor man's dwelling.
He opened up the door, and telling
The three to come in by the fire,
He fed each what he might require:
The horse was given a bellyful
Of barley; and the laboring bull
Of pulse; the dog, as table mate,
Was seated at a heaping plate.
For hospitality thus proffered,
And as some recompense, each offered
To give this hospitable man
His years of life. The horse began,
And gave his first; so and we find
In early years a spirited mind
In each of us. The bull gave second;
And so our middle years are reckoned
The time to work with industry
At gathering wealth. And finally
The dog gave his years last, they say.
And so, as we grow old and gray,
Son Branchus, we are peevish, and
Fawn only on the feeding hand;
We always bark, nor like the face
Of any stranger 'round the place.

75. *The Unskilled Doctor*

A doctor was unskilled. He said
To someone lying ill in bed
(Though everybody said, "Don't fear;
You'll live; it's chronic and severe;
You'll soon be better anyway"),
"I don't deceive, nor fashion snares:
You'd better order your affairs.
You will not last another day;
You're dying." This he said, and then
Made no more visits there again.
In time the other man returned,
Recovered from his woes, but burned
By fever, weak of leg, and yellow,
And met his friend the doctor fellow.
"Greetings," the doctor said. "Do tell,
How are they all below in Hell?"
"They're resting now," the sick man said,
"Drinking of Lethe with the dead.
But Cora and great Pluto now
Are starting up a fearful row,
And threatening doctors. You know why?
You don't allow the sick to die.
They plan to register each one—
You'll head the list when it is done.
But I was fearful, and drew nigh,
And touched their scepters, hoped to die,
And swore an oath it wasn't true—
You were no doctor; no, not you."

76. The Horseman and His Horse

A horseman whom the fates of war
Associated even more
Than customary with his horse
Throughout its every turn and course,
Had always fed it every day
With barley fodder and with hay,
Judging he had a noble steed,
A strong defender in his need.
But when the battles all had ended,
And peace had finally descended,
The horseman to his great dismay
Received no more his country's pay.
And so the horse must carry down
Logs from the woods above the town,
Could barely walk, and saved his soul
On wretched bran heaps which he stole.
He humbly carried on his back
No longer riders but a pack.
Then once again before the walls
Another war was heard, and calls
Upon the trumpet for all men
To clean their shields, and once again
To saddle up, and sharpen steel.
The horseman, hearing this appeal,
Bitted his horse, and led him by
In order that he might comply,
And ride. Alas! The poor horse fell,
No longer strong enough, nor well.
"Enlist among the infantry,"
The horse commanded. "As for me,
You've made your horse into an ass—
Can the reverse be brought to pass?"

77. The Raven and the Fox

A raven stopped when he had bitten
A piece of cheese. A fox, hard smitten
With longing for the cheese, deceived
The bird as follows: "I am grieved,
O raven, for although your wings
Are beautiful above all things,
And too, I see, your eye is bright,
Your neck is charming to the sight,
And like an eagle, you've a heart,
And talons, too, to take your part
Should any creature dare dispute—
You do not caw, for you are mute."
The raven, flattered, puffed, and proud,
Let go the cheese to cry out loud.
The wise fox took it with her tongue,
"You are not voiceless, then; you've sung.
Well, raven, that is evidence
You've everything," she said, "but sense."

78. The Sick Raven

A raven who was ill once said
To his poor mother, "Why, instead
Of weeping, mother, don't you pray
The gods to take my pain away?"
His mother then replied, "And who
Among the gods will rescue you?
Whose altar is there you have left
Untouched by sacrilegious theft?"

79. The Dog Carrying Meat

A dog once stole a piece of meat
Out of a shop, and down the street
She went, and walked beside a brook.
But in the stream she caught a look
At what seemed bigger there reflected;
And, moved by what she had detected,
She threw her piece of meat away.
But then she found to her dismay
She'd neither what she'd seen below
Nor what she'd been so quick to throw.

80. The Modest Camel

A master who was drinking made
His camel dance in masquerade
To brassy cymbals and a flute.
"I only wish," remarked the brute,
"That I might walk the road hereafter
Without arousing jeers and laughter,
Let alone foolishly resorting
To ballet dancing and contorting."

81. The Ape and the Fox

"That gravestone," said the ape, "you see,
My father handed down to me—
My father's father too," he cried.
"Lie as you wish," the fox replied,
"I have no proof of whether you
Are speaking false or speaking true."

82. The Lion, the Mouse, and the Fox

When sleep had lulled a lion's brain,
A little mouse ran through his mane.
With bristling hair the lion, irked,
Sprang from the lair in which he lurked.
The wily fox with scornful laughter
Remarked the lord of beasts was after
A mouse. "O knave," the lion said,
"I did not fear that as he fled
He'd nip my hide. For it was plain
He planned to dirty up my mane."

83. The Groom and the Horse

He passed each evening drinking up
His horse's barley, cup by cup,
But groomed him neatly every day.
The horse at last was heard to say,
"If you desire a handsome steed,
Don't sell the stuff on which I feed."

84. The Bull and the Gnat

Upon a bull's bent horn there lit
A gnat who waited there a bit;
Then, humming musically, said,
"If I weigh down and bow your head,
I'll sit down by the river side
Upon a tree." The bull replied,
"I care not if you stay or go,
For when you came I didn't know."

85. *The Dogs and the Wolves*

Between the dogs and wolves of late
There was an atmosphere of hate.
An old Achaean took command
As general of the canine land.
And, being wise in war, he waited.
But when they urged him on, he stated
The reasons he delayed. He said,
"Hear why I wait: I use my head.
It's always best to have a scheme.
The enemy I see all seem
To be one sort. By contrast we
Are some from Crete, and some may be
Molossians; among the best
Are Acarnanians; some of the rest
Are Dolopes, though others boast
They come from Thrace or Cyprus' coast,
And some from elsewhere. Why say more?
Our colors are at least a score,
And not just one like theirs, for we
Exhibit great variety:
Some black, some ash, some light of coat
But ticked with silver at the throat,
And others wholly white. And so
How might I ever hope to go
To war with such a mongrel lot
Against those matching spot for spot?"

86. The Fox Who Stuffed Herself

Once in the hollow at the foot
Of an old oak, beneath its root,
A goatherd's ragged knapsack lay,
All full of foodstuffs in decay.
A fox ran in, and ate the mess.
Her stomach, as of course you'd guess,
Was bloated, and she wasn't able
To leave her narrow dinner table.
Another fox while going by
Observed her plight, and heard her cry,
And said to her, "Just wait. For when
You're hungry, you'll be thin again."

87. The Hound and the Hare

A hound ran through the mountains where
He started up a little hare.
Pursuing her he tried to bite,
But when she turned around in fright,
He fawned as if upon a friend.
"Consistency I recommend,"
The hare remarked, "and at the least
Behavior like one kind of beast.
Are you a friend? Why bite? Or foe?
Pray, why then fawn upon me so?"

88. The Crested Lark and the Farmer

A certain lark who wore a crest
Was busy building him a nest
Deep in the foliage where his brood
Of children grew in solitude,
Already crested, big and strong.
One day the farmer came along,
Observed the land, and felt the heat.
"Now is the time to harvest wheat,"
He said, "It's time at last to call
My friends to help me reap it all."
One lark among the children heard,
And called his father, passed the word,
And urged him please to let them go.
The father listened, but said, "No.
It isn't time to set you free.
A man who counts on friends won't be
In any hurry." But the master
Observed the grain still growing faster
Under the radiance of the sun,
Promising reapers, when they'd done,
Wages tomorrow; and, said he,
The gleaners too will get their fee.
The lark then turned around, and said,
"Now children, it is time we fled.
When counting on himself, a man
Will work as quickly as he can."

89. The Wolf and the Lamb

A wolf once saw a little lamb
Strayed from the flock, and by a sham
And specious accusation thought
To get the dinner that he sought
Instead of snatching it by force,
  And thus began his sly discourse:
"You slandered me while small last year."
"A year ago I wasn't here;
  I'm not a last year's lamb," it squealed.
"Didn't you crop my private field?"
"I ate no grass, nor did I graze."
"Well then, you dried my stream for days
  By drinking it." "My drink, I vow,
  My mother's nipple gave 'til now."
That instant he picked up the lamb,
And said while eating it, "I am
A wolf you'll not make dinnerless,
No matter if each time I press
A claim, you answer everything,
Refuting every charge I bring."

90. The Raging Lion

A lion raged. A fawn who stood
And watched his madness from the wood
Said, "In his senses he is bad—
What won't he do when really mad!"

91. The Bull and the Goat

A bull who fled a lion's wrath
Encountered standing in his path
Within a mountain herdsman's cave
A maverick goat, which, acting brave,
Thrust out the horns upon its head.
"It isn't you," the big bull said,
"It is the lion that I fear.
Your insults, while my foe is near,
I'll stand a bit. Just let him go,
And pass me by, and then you'll know
How vast the difference, and full,
Between a mere goat and a bull."

92. The Timid Hunter and the Woodcutter

A hunter not untouched by fright
Once tracked a lion in its flight
On mountains under shadowing trees.
And happening on a man at ease,
An old woodcutter, near a pine,
He asked him, "Have you seen some sign
Of lion tracks? It's lurking near,
Down in some hole located here.
By all the mountain nymphs, do tell."
The old woodcutter answered, "Well,
It's with God's help you came, I'd say.
I'll show the lion right away."
But turning pale, with teeth a-chatter,
The hunter said to him, "No matter.
Don't give me more than I request.
Just show his tracks, but let him rest."

93. The Wolves, the Sheep, and the Ram

Some messengers came to the sheep,
Sent by the wolves, with oaths to keep
The peace secure, if they would bring
The dogs to them for punishing.
Because of these same dogs they fight,
And hate each other's very sight.
The stupid flock with aimless bleating
Were going to send them back a greeting,
But one great ram, already old,
Straightening higher in the fold
With all his deep fleece bristling, spoke:
"This is at least a novel stroke.
And how am I to live with you
Unguarded, when you are the crew
Who make it dangerous nowadays,
Though guarded by the dogs, to graze?"

94. The Wolf and the Heron

A wolf once had a bone stuck tight
Down in his gullet. In his plight
He told a heron if he'd go
'Way down into his throat below,
And then pull up the wretched thing,
And thus relieve his suffering,
He'd give him some appropriate pay.
He pulled it up, and right away
Requested payment as agreed.
The wolf with toothy grin indeed
Remarked, "You should be satisfied.
Your head's been in a wolf's inside;
You've got it out—undamaged too.
That should be pay enough for you."

95. The Lion, the Hind, and the Fox

A lion who was ill once lay
With sluggish limbs spread every way
Upon the earth and barren rocks,
And as a friend he had a fox
With whom he held this conversation:
"You can," he said, "be my salvation
In case you wish. I've set my heart
Upon a hind which dwells apart
Beneath wild pines in yonder wood,
And now I am no longer good
Or strong enough to hunt a deer.
You, if you please, shall bring her here,
And put her in my hands, enraptured
By your fine honeyed words, and captured."
The wily fox, on mischief bound,
Departed for the wood, and found
The hind upon the soft grass, playing;
And kissed her first to greet her, saying
She'd come to bring a pleasant word.
"The lion, as you may have heard,
Lives near me, but he feels so ill
And near to dying he must fill
His place as sovereign now. The pig
Is senseless, and the bear, though big,
Is sluggish, and the leopard hot
In temper, and the tiger not
Quite modest when impartially viewed,
And far too fond of solitude.
He deems the hind most fit of all
To be the sovereign; for she's tall,
She has a proud look, and she lives

For many years, and too, she gives
Affright to every crawling creature
With her great horns, a different feature
From those of bulls, far more like trees.
Why tell you more of things like these?
It has been settled anyhow;
You will be chosen ruler now
Of every mountain-roaming beast.
So let there be, I beg, at least
Some recollection in your mind
Of the poor fox, O mistress hind,
And that she was the first to tell.
That's why I came. But now farewell,
Dear friend. I hasten back again
In case the lion seeks me when
He needs some counsel (for he asks
Advice from me in all his tasks).
I think that you'll come too, my dear,
If you will only lend an ear
To this old hand. It's fitting, too,
For you will be at hand to do
Those little things, at least in part,
Which help his suffering, and give heart.
The little things have greatest powers
To win those living their last hours.
The soul of anyone who dies
Judges the loyal with the eyes."
So spoke the wily fox. The hind
Puffed with conceit by every kind
Of fabrication, went to see,
And did not know what was to be
When entering the lion's lair.
The lion, with more haste than care,

Rushed from his bed, nor stopped to pause,
And nicked her ears with tips of claws.
The wretched hind, impelled by fright,
Ran out the door in frantic flight
Into the middle of the wood.
The wily fox, frustrated, stood
And wrung her hands, her labor vain.
The lion bit his lips in pain,
And groaned, for he was hungry too.
Then to the fox he spoke anew,
And begged that she would find again
Some other trick. She racked her brain,
And said, "It's hard, this thing you ask,
But once again I'll try the task."
Then like a wise old hound she went
Along the traces of the scent,
Weaving all villainy and art,
And always asked in every part
What herdsmen had perhaps been seeing
A bloodstained hind as she was fleeing.
But anyone who saw the hind
Guided the fox, and helped her find
Her resting in a shady place
Recuperating from the race.
With face and brow untouched by shame
The fox stopped. With her heart aflame
And back and legs a-bristling hair
The hind spoke thus: "O wretch, beware
How you approach me, hateful one,
Or what you mutter you have done!
I tell you, you shall rue it! Go,
And play the fox with those who know
Still less than I; and try to string

Some other on, and make him king."
The fox's spirit was not daunted,
And as reproof to this she taunted,
"Are you so base-born, full of fear,
That you suspect your friends? Look here:
The lion, planning he would give
Advice, and change the way you live
From former sloth to energy,
Laid hands upon your ears. You see,
That's what a dying father'd do.
For he was going to give to you
His final words and last injunctions
So you might exercise your functions
When watching over such a realm
After you're seated at the helm.
You couldn't stand a scratch in play
From a frail hand, but pulled away
By force, and hurt yourself the more.
The anger that he has in store
Is more than yours. In trying you
He found you faithless—flippant, too—
And says he'll make the wolf the king.
A knavish master! What a thing!
What shall I do? You are the cause
Of all our ills. So do not pause,
But come! Be noble! Do not be
Dismayed like a poor sheep. But see!
By all the leaves and springs I vow
That just as I would gladly bow
My head as slave to you alone,
So will he place you on his throne.
He has no hate, nor wish to kill,
But offers you his best good will."

With wheedling words and honeyed breath
She coaxed the deer to go to death
A second time. And when she stood
Within the fastness of the wood,
The lion had himself a feast,
A royal one to say the least,
Guzzling flesh, and also sucking
The marrow from the bones while plucking
The choicest inward parts. His guide,
The thief, stood hungrily aside,
But on the sly she seized the heart,
And thus had profit for her part.
The lion counted all with care,
And found the heart alone not there,
And searched throughout his house and bed.
The wily fox, to fool him, said,
"You'll search in vain for one more part;
She simply didn't have a heart."

96. The Wolf and the Ram

A wolf once walked beside a wall.
A ram within was heard to call
Him nasty names while peeking out.
With gnashing teeth he turned about,
And said, "The place has called me names;
You have no cause for boasts or claims."

97. The Lion and the Bull

A hungry lion once campaigning
Against a wild bull, after feigning
To make oblation to the mother
Of all the gods, then asked the other
To come to dinner. The bull said
He'd come, not guessing where this led.
He came, and stopped before the door,
For when he saw upon the floor,
Lying beside it, many a pot
Of bronze, all full and boiling hot,
And sacrificial razors, knives,
All newly cleaned for taking lives,
Or flaying oxen, and he found
No other single thing around
Except a prisoner, chanticleer,
He thought it best to disappear
Up on the mountain far away.
The lion on a later day
Met him, and showered him with blame.
The bull replied to him, "I came;
I'll tell the augury. It said
Your offerings of food, instead
Of being what a bull could crop,
Were fitted for the butcher shop."

98. The Lion's Wooing

A tawny lion who was caught
By love for a young maid, besought
Her father that they might be wed.
Expressionless, the old man said
(Not showing him dislike or hate),
"I give her to you as your mate,
Rejoicing in the giving, too,
As anyone would gladly do.
For who would not delight to be
Allied with lion's majesty?
The heart of maiden or of child,
However, is not bold; you're wild;
You bear great teeth and such great claws
Would not a timid maiden pause
Before embracing you, from fear?
Or seeing you, not shed a tear?
In face of all these things, pray tarry;
Consider (if you wish to marry),
And then no longer be a beast,
But turn into a groom at least."
The lion was excited, and,
Sure of the gift, with his own hand
Pulled out his teeth, and had each claw
Cut out; then showed his father-in-law,
Demanding that he give the bride.
But no one now was on his side,
And someone hit him with a brick,
And someone struck him with a stick,
And someone with his hand. He lay
Limp as a pig, and passed away.

99. The Eagle and the Lion

An eagle chanced to overtake
A lion whom he sought to make
His partner. Said the lion, "Sure!
But first, to make the deal secure,
You'll give your wings to me as pledge
You'll not abuse the privilege.
For how shall I have faith you'll be
A friend when you don't stay with me?"

100. The Dog and the Wolf

A dog who happened to be stout
Once met a wolf who asked about
How he was reared that he'd become
So much more full of fat than some.
"A man," he said, "just fed me well."
"But what about your neck? Do tell,"
The other said, "why it is bare."
"I wore an iron collar there
Which he who reared me forged to fit.
It rubbed my flesh a little bit."
The wolf let out a roar of laughter,
"To such a luxury hereafter,"
He said, "I'll say goodbye—and gladly,
For iron chafes my neck too badly."

101. The Wolf Called Lion

Among the wolves a wolf there was,
His nickname "Lion," called because
He was so powerful and great.
Alas, he could not bear the weight
Of so much glory in his heart,
And pridefully he kept apart,
Conversing with the lions instead.
A wily fox observed, and said,
"Let me not be elated quite
To your insane, demented height,
For just as you indeed appear
A lion among wolves, I fear
That you're a wolf as plain as day
Among the lions where you stay."

102. The Lion's Reign

A certain lion used to reign;
He was not savage, bold, nor vain,
Rejoicing in the strength to strike,
But gentle, just, and almost like
A man. During his reign indeed
The animals all came to plead
Their cases, and to give account:
The wolf with lamb; the catamount
With goat; the tiger with the deer;
And all have peace forever here.
The cowering hare was heard to say,
I have been praying for this day—
'Twill make the feeble and the small
More fearsome than the strong and tall."

103. The Lion and the Fox

A lion who was getting weak,
And was no longer fit to seek
His meals by hunting (for he'd grown
Old long ago) lay all alone
And weary in his hollow den
As if in sickness, now and then
Gasping for breath, although with guile,
But not in truth, and all the while
Pretended his deep voice was small.
Then rumor paid the beasts a call,
And all the beasts were grieved to know
The lion was so ill and low;
So each one entered in to see
And visit him. In sequence he
Ate them all up; no longer weak,
He found his old age fat and sleek.
A clever fox—suspicious too—
Standing afar asked, "How are you,
O king?" The lion said, "My dear,
I greet you. But you are not near.
Why look upon me from afar?
Come here, sweet creature that you are,
Console me from nearby, and tell
The stories you recount so well."
"May you be saved," the vixen said,
"But if I go away instead,
Please understand what holds me back.
For I have noticed many a track
Of beasts who entered, but I doubt
That you can show one coming out."

104. The Dog

There was a dog who used to bite
Just out of treachery and spite.
His master forged for him a bell
To make him known and warn as well.
He swaggered through the market place,
And shook his bell in every face
Until an old bitch cried aloud,
"You silly fool, why are you proud?"

105. The Wolf and the Lion

A wolf who stole a sheep one day
From out the flock was on his way
To take it home. A lion came,
And snatched the sheep. With rage aflame
The wolf stood well aside, and howled,
"Unfair! It's mine!" The lion growled
In mockery, "So you contend
You got it fairly from a friend?"

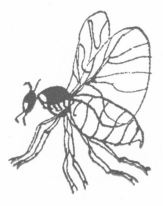

106. The Lion, the Fox, and the Ape

A lion tried to emulate
The noble life of men of state.
Within his den he passed each day,
And those he thought in every way
Were noblest of the mountain strain
He tried his best to entertain.
A crowd of every sort of creature
Came to his cave. He made a feature
Of entertaining every guest,
And feeding all the most and best.
He'd taken in a wily fox
To share his house beneath the rocks,
And with her lived most pleasantly.
But with them too there chanced to be
A certain ape who carved the meat,
And gave his messmates shares to eat,
Who, if a stranger ever came,
Put down before him just the same
The lion had upon his plate,
It was the freshest food they ate.
The wily fox had for her share
Unequal portions and unfair,
For it was stale and meager diet.
One time, intentionally quiet,
She kept her hand away from dinner,
And didn't put much food within her.
The lion, asking what was wrong,
Said, "Clever fox, do come along!
Pray talk as usual. Condescend
To put your shining face, my friend,
Into some portion of the feast."
But she replied, "O bravest beast,
I'm searching through my heart with care.

The present state of things I'll bear;
It's for the future that I fear.
If day by day while dining here
These strangers enter, one by one,
Or if it's regularly done,
Then I alone, it cannot fail,
Will eat what's even worse than stale."
Amused, the lion grinned. Said he,
"Just blame the ape for that, not me."

107. The Lion and the Mouse

A lion with a mouse he'd caught
Was going to dine. The mouse, distraught,
Poor house-born thief of every room,
Was reckless, being near his doom,
And begged and whined in some such way:
"It's fitting that you hunt and slay
Deer and horn-bearing bulls to fill
Your belly full of flesh. But still
A dinner just of mouse is small,
And barely fills your mouth at all.
Have mercy please, I beg of you.
Perhaps some honor I can do
Will serve as thanks; I'm small, I know."
Laughing, the great beast let him go.
But youthful hunters whom he met
Caught him, and tied him in a net.
Then from a hole the mouse appeared,
And with his little sharp teeth sheared
The tough mesh of the net, and freed
The lion, giving life, his meed,
The recompense that was his due,
For thus he saved the lion too.

Prologue II

This tale's an ancient find, O son
Of Emperor Alexander, one
That Syrian men who lived around
Ninus' and Belus' time once found.
But first, they say, these tales were told
To children of the Greeks by old
Wise Aesop; and Kibysses, who
Told stores to the Libyans too.
But new and jingling verse I write,
Like warhorse trappings, golden bright.
When I had opened up the door,
Others went in to Aesop's store,
But brought out verses too involved,
Like riddles that are never solved.
For all they learned, that clever crowd,
Was how to cry the tales out loud,
No matter whether far or near.
The fables that I tell are clear;
The teeth of my iambics I
Don't sharpen, but instead I try
To temper all their points with fire,
And soften that you may admire.
And so a second time I bring
This book of fables that I sing.

108. The Field Mouse and the House Mouse

Among the mice was one who led
A simple field mouse life; instead
The other lurked in hole and bin
And storeroom which were rich within.
They held their lives up to compare,
And see which had the better share.
Now first the house mouse came to dine
When fields were blooming green and fine.
He nibbled slender roots of grain
In lumps all black and wet from rain.
He said, "The life you revel in
Is like an ant's; your loaves are thin,
And you must eat them in a ditch.
But as for me, I'm truly rich;
The horn of Amalthea's mine
In contrast with the way you dine.
If you will only come with me,
You'll see what luxury can be
Without this digging like a mole."
Persuading him to see his hole
Beneath the wall of some man's house,
He led away the farmer mouse.
He showed him barley piled in heaps,
And all the pulse the master keeps;
He showed him jars of figs and honey,
All sticky, sweet, and rather runny;
And dates in baskets in a pile.
Rejoicing in these things a while
He dragged a cheese across the floor
When someone opened up the door.
He leaped away at once to race

From danger in such narrow space
Down in the mousehole taking flight,
And screamed and jabbered, mad with fright,
Making his host feel most distressed
At what had happened to his guest.
He paused a minute; then peeked out,
And gaining courage was about
To touch a Camirean fig
When someone else—and also big—
Came to pick up some other thing
Out of the storeroom; cowering,
The mice kept hidden well inside.
The field mouse said, "You may abide,
Rejoice, and feel that you are rich,
And revel in these dinners which
You have alone. I'm leaving you.
For there are many dangers too,
And I myself shall not refrain
From simple clods of earth, and grain
From which to gnaw the loaves I've made.
And not forever be afraid."

109. The Crab and His Mother

Once to a crab his mother said
Not to go sideways, but ahead,
Nor drag his limbs from side to side
On ledges moist from ebbing tide.
The crab said, "Mother, kindly teach:
Go straight yourself along the beach,
And I shall keep my eye on you,
And if you do it, I shall too."

110. The Man and His Dog

A traveler, who wished to go,
Addressed his bitch, who dawdled, so:
"Get everything packed up! Prepare!
You're coming with me. So why stare?"
She raised her tail behind to say,
"I'm set. You're causing the delay."

111. *The Peddler and His Ass*

A peddler heard that near the deep
The salt was plentiful and cheap,
And wishing some, he piled a load
Upon his ass. But on the road,
Bringing it home, the poor beast tripped,
And unintentionally slipped
Into a stream in sudden fright.
Some salt dissolved, and feeling light,
He stood up easier, and went
On inland, feeling more content.
The salt was sold, and as before
The man then loaded up with more,
Making the burden greater still,
And drove the ass along until
He crossed the river, sore distressed.
And there on purpose, and with zest,
He fell down where he fell before,
Dissolving all the salt he bore,
And stood up nimbly, greatly pleased
At the advantage he had seized.
The trader pondered as he rode,
Then later carried home a load
Of porous sponges from the sea,
For salt was hateful as could be.
Once more they reached the river. Then
The ass, on purpose, fell again;
But all at once the load was wet,
The sponges swelled up bigger yet,
So that he went, that scheming jack,
With twice the burden on his back.

112. *The Mouse and the Bull*

A mouse once bit a bull. In pain
He chased the mouse, but all in vain:
The mouse fled far ahead, and stole
Into the fastness of his hole.
The bull stood, digging with his horn
Until, becoming tired and worn,
He squatted down, and went to sleep
Beside the hole. From 'way down deep
The mouse first peeked, then crept ahead,
Bit him again, and once more fled.
The bull sprang quickly to his feet,
And his confusion was complete.
The mouse just murmured to the bull,
"The big aren't always powerful.
Sometimes the lowly and the small
Are the most powerful of all."

113. *The Shepherd and His Dog*

A man was gathering his stock
Into the fold, and planned to lock
A wolf within it for the night.
His dog observed, and said, "You might
Tell how you hope to save your sheep
When bringing him in here to sleep."

114. The Lamp

While drunk with oil, a lamp was boasting
To all on hand one evening, toasting
His light as brilliant, stronger far,
And brighter than the evening star;
It shone on all remarkably.
But when the wind came whistling, he
Went out at once, struck by a blast.
But someone lit him up at last,
And said, "Shine, lamp; but hold your peace.
The light of stars will never cease."

115. The Tortoise and the Eagle

A sluggish tortoise one time said
To terns and gulls in marshes bred,
"Would they had made me wingèd too."
By chance an eagle, passing through,
Heard her, and said, "And how much pay
Will be the eagle's share, I pray,
If I should make you light as air?"
"I'll give you all that's rich and rare,
The Indian Ocean's gifts." "Then I
Shall teach you," said the bird, "to fly."
Lifting her upside down, he flew
Into the clouds, from whence he threw
Her on the mountain where she fell,
And struck, and broke her brittle shell.
She said while dying, "It is right
That I should die. For wingèd flight
And airy clouds I've little call,
Who barely move on land at all."

116. The Man and the Boy

Once in the middle of the night
A boy sang sweetly by the light
Of the bright moon. A woman, hearing,
Got up, went to the window, peering,
And saw the boy, all fair and shining.
Leaving her husband still reclining,
She went below, and out the door,
And had her wish for something more.
Her husband woke up suddenly,
And looked to see where she might be,
But could not find his wandering spouse
In any place inside the house;
So went himself down to the street,
And said to her, "Don't fear, my sweet.
The boy can sleep with us, you know."
They took him in with them. And so
The boy, since both desired to play,
Had relaxation in that way.

117. *The Man, the Ants, and Hermes*

A ship once sank with all its crew.
Some who saw it said he knew
The gods had all decided wrong,
For though one man had gone along
Who was profane, yet just the same
The rest who died were not to blame.
Now while he spoke it came to pass
A swarm of ants came through the grass
Eager to nibble on the wheat.
Bitten by one, he stamped his feet
Upon the rest, and walked beyond.
But Hermes struck him with his wand,
And said to him, "Won't you permit
The immortal gods the right to sit
As judges of your actions, though
You judge these little ants below?"

118. *The Swallow and the Snake*

A twittering swallow, man's best neighbor,
Each spring, with patience and with labor,
Used to arrange her nest somewhere
Within a courthouse wall, and there
She mothered seven little things,
Not yet bright purple in their wings.
A snake came creeping from its hole,
And, one after another, stole
And ate them all. Unhappily
Lamenting the catastrophe
To her poor brood, untimely dead,
The miserable mother said,
"Alas for my sad lot, because
From that same place where men have laws
And statutes too, and equity,
A swallow badly wronged I flee."

119. The Wooden Hermes

There was a Hermes made of wood,
Owned by a craftsman. This man stood
Pouring libations every day,
And sacrificing, yet, some way
He still was poor. Enraged at last
He raised the statue up, and cast
It to the ground. Its broken head
Ran gold. Collecting this, he said,
"Hermes, you've been unkind, unfair,
And for your friends you do not care;
To worshippers you are no use.
But when we heap on you abuse,
These many riches you've repaid.
I didn't know, and hadn't made,
As now hereafter I shall do,
This newest reverence to you."

120. The Frog Who Was a Doctor

Inhabitant of marsh and pool,
Rejoicing in the shade and cool,
The frog who lives on either hand
Beside the ditches, came to land,
And to the animals declared,
"I am a doctor, well prepared;
I know such things as no one knows,
Not even Paeon, though he goes
As doctor to the gods on high."
A fox said, "How can you apply
Your skills to cure another fellow,
When you can't keep from being yellow?"

121. The Bird and the Cat

A bird one time grew ill and weak.
A cat leaned over her to speak:
"How are you? Tell me what you need,
For I'll provide it with all speed.
But do take care." The bird's reply:
"If you go 'way, I shall not die."

122. The Ass and the Wolf

An ass once trod upon a thorn,
And, being lamed, he stopped, forlorn.
But seeing that a wolf was nigh,
And fearing he would surely die,
He spoke thus to the wolf, and said:
"I'm going to die; I'm nearly dead;
But just the same I'm glad we met,
For you shall be the one to get
My poor remains; no carrion crow
Or vulture'll dine on me. And so
Do me an easy favor, taking
This thorn out of my foot, thus making
It easy for my soul to go
To Hades' realm far down below."
"This favor I will gladly do,"
The wolf replied to him, and drew
The hot thorn out between his teeth.
The ass, no longer held beneath
The weight of pain and great distress,
Kicked yellow-boy with such success
He hadn't time to shut his jaws,
Then fled, with barely time to pause
To beat him on the nose and head.
"Alas," the wolf in sorrow said,
"I suffer this with justice. Why
Was I persuaded now to try
To treat the lame, when from the start
I'd only learned the butcher's art?"

123. The Hen Who Laid the Golden Eggs

A good hen laid some golden eggs . . .

124. The Hunter, the Partridge, and the Cock

A friend came to a hunter who
Planned making thyme and parsley do
For dinner, as he hadn't caught
A single bird. His cage held nought.
Indeed he was about to slay
A speckled partridge anyway,
A tame one kept for hunting birds,
But it besought him with these words:
"Hereafter," said it, "don't forget:
You cannot use your hunting net,
For who will quickly bring in view
Keen-sighted flocks of birds for you?
And what sweet songster will you keep
To help to put yourself to sleep?"
He let the partridge go, and said
A wattled cock would do instead.
But from its perch it loudly cried,
"What will you do when I have died,
How learn how long is left 'til dawn
After your hour-prophet's gone?
Will it be possible to know
Orion of the Golden Bow
Has settled for the night? And who
Will tell of morning tasks to do
When dew is on the thrush's wings?"
"I know you're useful for some things,"
The man replied, "but I repeat:
My friend needs something he can eat."

125. The Playful Ass

A certain ass climbed to the roof,
And broke the tiling with his hoof
While playing there. One of the men
Ran up, and led him down again,
And beat him with a stick. The beast
Turned when the man at last had ceased,
And said to him, "My back is sore;
And yesterday, or day before,
The ape delighted all of you
By doing just the things I do."

126. The Traveler and Truth

A man who traveled chanced to stray
Into the wilderness one day
Where Truth was standing all alone.
He said to her, "Pray tell, old crone,
What reason did you have that led
To living in the wilds instead
Of in the city?" In reply
The learned thinker said, "The Lie
Was found at first among but few.
Now, if it may be said, and you
Would care at all to stop and hear,
Man's life is worse than that, I fear."

127. *Zeus the Judge*

Zeus ordered Hermes heap in bins
Potsherds inscribed with all men's sins,
And giving justice, looked at all.
And as the sherds pile up, they fall
Into the hands of Zeus, one slow,
One quick, that he may sometime know,
And call them to account. So none
Need marvel if a rogue who's done
Evil too early, finds too late
That faring badly is his fate.

128. The Sheep and the Dog

A sheep addressed a shepherd thus:
"When you have finished clipping us,
    You have our fleece; our milk you drink,
    You like its curds as well, I think;
    You have our lambs in numbers too.
    We get no profit as do you;
    Instead our food is from the ground
    If any cheap is ever found
    Upon the mountains. Yet you feed
    This dog, supply his every need,
    And with the same solicitude
    As for yourself, you give him food."
    The dog heard this, and thus replied:
"Unless I came, and sat beside,
    And went among you to and fro,
    You never would have eaten so,
    Nor had good grazing any place.
    But I go running 'round, and chase
    Bandits and roguish sneak-thieves too,
    And any wolves pursuing you."

129. The Ass and the Little Dog

A man who had an ass once kept
A table-fed young dog, that lept
Around its master every way,
Rejoicing in its rhythmic play;
Its master hugged it close to heart.
The ass, however, for his part
Was left to run on tired feet,
And grind the everlasting wheat
Of dear Demeter through the night,
And through the day from on the height
He brought in wood, or from the field
Whatever crops it chanced to yield.
And in the courtyard fettered fast
Beside his crib, for his repast
Had barley grits, his usual due.
And burned by envy at the view
Of the young whelp in luxury,
And wailing most prodigiously,
He broke the chain and rope right off
That held him to his feeding trough,
Went to the middle of the yard,
And kicked immoderately hard.
And while he fawned and skipped about,
He threw the dishes round about,
And broke the table, smashed the chairs,
Then kissed his master unawares
At dinner, treading on his back.
The servants, seeing this attack,
Rescued their sore beleaguered master
From peril of extreme disaster,
Beating the beast upon his hide

With dogwood clubs from every side
Until the ass, expiring, said,
"By what misfortune was I led
To suffer so? Why didn't I
Run with the mules? Why did I try
So foolishly to measure up
To all the antics of a pup?"

130. The Fox and the Wolf

A fox had stopped not far away
From where a baited snare-trap lay,
And was considering which to do
Of all the tricks she had in view.
A wolf, who saw the fox, came near
To take the meat. The fox said, "Here!
Come take it and rejoice. I give
With friendship to my relative."
The wolf came closer, leaned to look,
And stooping over it, he shook
The stick; the rod, released, arose,
And struck him on the brow and nose.
"If you give friends such gifts in greeting,
What friend," he said, "will wish a meeting?"

131. The Profligate Young Man and the Swallow

A youth whom playing dice bereft
Of wealth, had only one cloak left,
And as it still was winter time,
And fields were white with frost and rime,
He suffered, shivering and blue.
But time in turn stripped this off too.
A swallow came before the spring
From lower Thebes, misreckoning
The season, and was far ahead.
He heard her chirping, and he said,
"What need have I for winter wear?
This swallow says it will be fair."
And as he spoke, he went again,
Consorted with the dice, and when
He'd played a little, lost once more,
And parted with the cloak he wore.
But snow and hail began to fall,
And there was need of clothes for all.
Naked within, he stuck his head
Outdoors, and saw the bird, and said,
"You wretch, I only wish that when
You came I hadn't seen you then.
For now this fraud has been repeated:
Not only you, but I've been cheated."

132. *The Sheep and the Wolf*

A lonely sheep began to flee
A wolf she noticed suddenly,
And went within an unlocked fold
Where festival they chanced to hold.
The wolf came not within the wall,
But stood outside with wheedling call:
"That altar's stained with blood. Beware!
They'll catch, and sacrifice you there.
Come out!" The sheep said, "Never fear
About my safety while I'm here,"
She said, "for I'm well off, you see.
For after all, I'd rather be
Fed to a god by some poor sinner
Than given to a wolf for dinner."

133. *The Ass and the Fox*

An ass one time was busy eating
Spines from a thorny shrub. In greeting
A fox said, "Tell me, in what way
You soften up hard food, I pray,
And eat it without being stung
With such a soft and supple tongue?"

The tail belonging to a snake
No longer thought it right to make
The head the leader, and declined
To creep, and follow it behind,
"For I," it said, "should lead a bit."
The other parts replied to it,
"You'll not do, leading. If you lead,
How will you guide us, wretch, indeed,
When you have neither eyes nor nose
By means of which each creature goes
Wherever passage is expected,
Or legs and feet can be direct?"
The head, alas, did not persuade
The tail; the thinking part obeyed;
The never-thinking part then led
The body and the neck and head,
And dragged it in a crazy dance,
Taking it backward, all by chance,
Until it landed in a hollow,
A cleft of rock where none could follow,
And on the rocks it crushed its spine.
The tail, once proud, began to whine,
And fawned, and begged, "O mistress head,
Do save us if you will instead.
For of this silly strife I've had,
The consequence is really bad."

135. *The Partridge and the Weasel*

He bought a partridge which he sent
To run in his establishment;
It took his fancy. It began
Its customary cry, and ran
Down the extent of the whole court,
And when it reached the steps, stopped short.
An evil-plotting weasel said,
"Well, who are you? Where were you bred?
Where have you been? And where abide?"
"I've just been bought," the bird replied.

. . . .
. . . .

"I also spend much time here, for
My mouse-devouring mother bore
Me here within, and yet I keep
Quite quiet, and I always creep
Into the farthest depths. But you,
Just purchased, as you say, as new,
Have come here, and can freely talk,"
The weasel said, "and raise a squawk."

136. The Ant and the Cicada

In winter time an ant was dragging
The food he'd stored, across the flagging,
And cooling what he'd heaped and had
In summer. A cicada bade
The ant (for he was starved) to give
Some food to him that he might live.
"What did you do," the other cried,
"Last summer?" "I have nought to hide.
I hadn't time to work; I passed
The time in singing." Shutting fast
His store of wheat, the other laughed,
And launched at him this parting shaft:
"Dance in the winter, if you please
To sing in summer at your ease."

137. The Galli Beggars

An ass was sold one time, and shared
By Galli beggars. He had fared
Unfortunately, and was weighted
With cures for thirst and hunger, fated
To bear the equipment of their trade
For these star players. So they made
Their rounds through every village, bent
On getting dainties as they went—
It was their wont. For who among
The rustics had not heard it sung
How Attis had been mutilated?
Who would not dance all animated,
And from his harvest offer some
First fruits for Rhea's holy drum?

138. The Ass Bearing a Statue

A villager once walked ahead,
A statue on the ass he led,

. . . .

139. The Spotted Lizard

A spotted lizard once detected
A spider's loom all unexpected,
And from the wall with rapid stroke
He cut himself a fine-spun cloak.

. . . .

140. The Drawings

In order to beguile his pain,
And find some means to entertain
He drew upon the walls around
Drawings of animals he'd found.

. . . .

141. The Oak Trees

A farmer will not have an ax
Unless you grow the wood he lacks.

.   .   .   .

142. The Peacock and the Crane

A peacock and a Libyan crane
Ate verdant grass upon a plain.

.   .   .   .

# NOTES

Although I have not attempted the same thing in English, the fables in the original Greek are arranged alphabetically according to the first letter of the first work of each. The first 123 are based upon the Mount Athos manuscript and go from A to O. The remaining fables are based upon the Vatican manuscript, and in them the alphabetical arrangement is abandoned. It is evident that there must have been at least 80 more fables in the Babrian collection.

Here are a few comments:

FABLE 12. This refers to the story of Procne and Philomela. See "Itys" in Names and Places, below.

FABLE 14. Even today they say that bears will not touch a dead body.

FABLE 19. Babrius clearly says, "green," and not "sour."

FABLE 31. This fable and the one following present a problem in scholarship with which I am not prepared to cope. The word which I have translated as "weasel" means "cat" in the modern literary tonge, the *catharevoussa*. At some point the meaning of the word changed. Which should we do, follow the modern Greeks, or go back to the classical age? It is true, of course, that we think of cats rather than weasels as the traditional enemies of mice. I don't know what Babrius thought.

FABLE 34. The sacrifices of the Greeks were usually banquets. The gods may indeed have been served first, but their share was not fit for human consumption.

FABLE 46. "His second fourth of life. . . ." What Babrius actually says is, "His second 'crow' . . ." in reference to Hesiod's lines, "The crow lives nine generations of men, the deer four generations of the crow. . . ."

FABLE 73. A kite belongs to the hawk family.

FABLE 79. In another version the dog crossed a bridge.

FABLE 106. This fable reflects the manners of the rich in the late empire: Babrius is the fox, his patron the lion. The fable is obviously incomplete.

PROLOGUE II. This Prologue is in this location solely because in the Greek it begins with the letter *M*, which is appropriate for the place. The fables of the first and second books which Babrius wrote are inextricably mixed. We are not even sure whether the second volume was a revision of the first or a new set of fables; probably the latter.

FABLE 123. Well known from prose versions found elsewhere.

FABLE 131. Lower Thebes means Thebes in Egypt.

FABLE 136. Usually translated as grasshopper, but I suspect the actual insect was probably the cicada.

FABLE 138. As the ass was led through the village streets, all the people bowed down in reverence to the statue. "Well!" said the owner of the ass, "Things have come to a pretty pass when people bow down to an ass!"

NAMES
AND
PLACES

The only proper names which have been omitted from this index are Aesop, Athens, Crete, Cyprus, the Indian Ocean, Libya, and Syria. Aesop is discussed in the Preface, and the others hardly need explanation.

Acarnania	A district on the west coast of Greece, north of the Gulf of Corinth.
Achaeans	Inhabitants of a district just south of the Gulf of Corinth. In Homer the name is equivalent to the name Greek.
Alcmene's son	Heracles.
Alexander	Alexander Severus, Roman emperor from A.D. 222 to 235. He was a Syrian, born in Palestine in A.D. 208.
Amalthea	A Cretan nymph who brought up the infant Zeus on the milk of a goat. The horn of the goat was given her by Zeus with the promise that she should always find in it whatever she wished.
Aphrodite	Goddess of love and beauty, who rose from the foam of the sea and stepped ashore on Cyprus; hence she is known as Cypris, the Cyprian.
Apollo	God of light, son of Zeus and Leto, twin brother of Artemis, goddess of the chase. Immediately after his birth he slew the dragon Python with the first shot of his bow.

Ares	God of war, son of Zeus and Hera. He was quarrelsome and blood-thirsty, disliked by the other gods, and usually lost his battles.
Athena	Goddess of war, who sprang fully armed from the head of her father, Zeus. She is the virgin goddess, patroness of the household arts, particularly spinning and weaving, the goddess of wisdom, and usually won her battles. Also known as Pallas Athene.
Attis	A beautiful youth, beloved of the goddess Rhea, or Cybele. He was driven to madness by her because he wished to wed another. He fled to the mountains, mutilated himself, and died. Rhea begged that his body might never know corruption.
Belus	The son of Libya and the father of Aegyptus. The latter subdued the land of the Malampodes ("Black-feet"), and named it "Egypt" for himself.
Boeotia	A district in Greece north of Athens. It was predominantly agricultural, and its inhabitants were noted for their rustic character.
Branchus	Probably the son of the emperor Alexander Severus.
Camirean figs	Figs from the city of Camirus in western Rhodes.
Cora	Daughter of Zeus and Demeter, and wife of Hades, the king of the world of the dead below. While plucking flowers, she was carried off by Hades. To appease her mother's wrath, Zeus sent Hermes to bring her back, but as she had already eaten part of a pomegranate given her by Hades, she could only come back part of the year. Her name means "maiden," and she is also known as Persephone.

Cypris	*See* Aphrodite.
Demeter	Goddess of agriculture and harvests, the daughter of Cronus and Rhea.
Dolopes	This name suggests the meaning, "tricksters."
Galli beggars	Emasculated beggar priests of Rhea.
Gardens of the West	There is no such place: the phrase is used as we use the phrase "Mountains of the Moon."
Golden Age	There were said to have been four ages of mankind: (1) the Golden Age, when all men lived happily; (2) the Silver Age, when all men lived in the condition of children; (3) the Brazen Age, when all implements were made of brass, and men of gigantic strength and stature destroyed each other; and (4) the Iron Age, when all men must labor. The present age is the Iron Age.
Hades	God of the lower world and of the dead, brother of Zeus and of Poseidon. In time the name was used to denote the lower world itself.
Heracles	Greek hero, the son of Zeus and Alcmene. He was renowned for his phenomenal strength. He was born in Thebes.
Hermes	The son of Zeus and the Naiad Maia, god of boundaries (which were marked by square posts of stone or wood, sometimes surmounted by the head of Hermes), roads, thievery, and gymnastic skill. He was also messenger of the gods, conductor of the souls of the dead on their way to the lower world, god of sleep and dreams, and the discoverer of music.
Iris	Goddess of the rainbow, and messenger of the gods.
Itys	Son of Tereus and of Procne. Tereus, pretending that Procne was dead, seduced her sister Philomela and cut her tongue out so that she

could not tell about it. However, she managed to do so, and in revenge the two sisters slew Itys and served him up for dinner for his father Tereus to eat. When Tereus learned what he had eaten, he was about to slay both sisters, but Zeus changed one into a swallow and the other into a nightingale.

Kybisses   A Libyan teller of fables. The name may be nothing but the result of a succession of errors in copying (Libysses = Kibysses = Kybisses), and therefore mean only, "the Libyan."

Lethe   A river in the lower world where the dead drink forgetfulness of their former lives.

Molossians   The inhabitants of the district of Epirus in western Greece.

Momus   The evil spirit of blame, mockery, and fault-finding.

Muse   One of the nymphs or goddesses who represent various kinds of poetry, art, or science. There were usually said to be nine, but the number was not fixed.

Nemesis   The personification of moral indignation, who inevitably punishes wanton arrogance.

Ninus   Another form of the name "Ninevah," capital of ancient Assyria, here personified.

Olympus   A mountain in Thessaly in northeastern Greece; the home of the gods.

Orion   A mythical hunter of gigantic size and strength. He pursued the sisters known as the Pleiades for five years until Zeus made them all into stars.

Paeon   In Homer, physician of the gods. Later the name was transferred to Apollo in his character of "healer" or "savior."

Pallas	*See* Athena.
Pan	God of flocks, herdsmen, and huntters; half-man, half-goat.
Phoebus	*See* Apollo.
Pleiades	The seven daughters of Atlas and the Ocean nymph Pleione, who were pursued by Orion for five years until Zeus turned them into stars. The rising of their constellation in the middle of May announced the approach of harvest; their setting announced the new sowing.
Pluto	Another name of Hades.
Poseidon	The god of the sea, brother of Zeus and Hades.
Prometheus	A Titan, brother of Atlas. He stole fire from heaven and gave it to mankind. For this he was chained to a rock while an eagle ate his liver. Prometheus was said to have molded men and animals from clay and to have animated them with the heavenly fire.
Pygmies	A race of diminutive people who lived in Africa. The cranes were said to fly to the land of the Pygmies in winter time. There were many fierce battles between the Pygmies and the cranes.
Rhea	Daughter of Uranus (heaven) and Gaea (earth), wife of Cronus, and mother of Zeus, Hades, Hera, Poseidon, Hestia, and Demeter. She was identified with the Asiatic goddess Cybele, the "Great Mother," whose priests were the emasculated Galli.
Tanagra	A town in eastern Boeotia, about fourteen miles from Thebes.
Thebes	The principal city of Boeotia, thirty-three miles northwest of Athens. Also the name of a city in Egypt on the Nile.

Theseus	The founder and earliest king of Athens, son of Aegeus, the victor in many adventures with monsters, the best known of which was his slaying of the Minotaur with the help of Ariadne, who gave him a ball of thread to unroll when he entered the Labyrinth, so that he was able to find his way out after slaying the monster.
Thrace	The farthest northeastern district of Greece.
Zeus	The greatest of the gods, son of Cronus and Rhea, brother of Poseidon and Hades, with whom he divided the world, Zeus obtaining the heaven, Poseidon the sea, and Hades the lower world. As the god of the sky, he is the god of weather, gathers clouds, sends rain or snow, and hurls the thunderbolts.

INDEX
TO
FABLES

PRINTED IN U.S.A.